Usborne
First Sticker Book
Nativity

Felicity Brooks

Designed by Meg Dobbie

Illustrated by

Ag Jatkowska

You can find all the stickers
at the back of the book.

Going to Bethlehem

A long, long time ago, Mary and Joseph had to go to the little town of Bethlehem. Mary was going to have a baby. She was very tired, so she rode on a donkey.

No room at the inn

Mary and Joseph needed somewhere to stay, but Bethlehem was very busy. "We have no rooms left," said the innkeeper, "but you can stay in the stable at the back if you want to."

A boy is born

That night Mary's baby was born in the stable.
Joseph made a soft bed for him in the manger
and Mary named the new baby Jesus.

Shepherds in the fields

In the fields near Bethlehem, some shepherds were watching over their sheep. Suddenly they saw a very bright light shining in the night sky.

Amazing angels

Then the sky was filled with beautiful angels.
"Don't be afraid," said one of the angels. "I have good news.
Tonight a baby has been born who is the Son of God.
Go to Bethlehem and find him."

The shepherds arrive

The shepherds ran into Bethlehem and found the baby asleep in the stable. They told Mary and Joseph what the angel had said about Jesus.

The Three Wise Men

Far, far away, three wise men saw a big, bright star moving across the sky. They knew it meant something special had happened, so they followed the star to Bethlehem.

The Nativity

The wise men brought gifts of gold,
frankincense and myrrh for Jesus.
This was the first Christmas day
and everyone was very happy.

Going to Bethlehem

Donkey

Mary

Joseph

No room at the inn

Mary

Joseph

Innkeeper

A boy is born

Baby Jesus

Shepherds in the fields

Amazing angels

Gloria! Gloria! Gloria!

The shepherds arrive

The Three Wise Men

The Nativity

Baby Jesus

Three Wise Men

Joseph and Mary

Shepherds